SPRINT READING SKILLS PROGRAM

STORY BOOK

FIRST LEVEL

Scholastic Book Services

New York Toronto London Auckland Sydney Tokyo

Editor
Les Purificación

SPRINT Reading Programs Director
Ray Shepard

Art Director
Skip Sorvino

Design
Christopher Austopchuk

Production
Jeanette Zelhof

Illustrations:
Donald Brautigam:
Pages 80, 82–83, 85, 86.
Sal Catalano:
Pages 46, 49, 50.
Warren Frick:
Pages 64–65, 66–67, 69, 70–71, 72.
Susannah Kelly:
Pages 94–95, 96, 97, 99, 100, 103, 104, 106,
115, 116–117, 119, 120.
Tim Lewis:
Pages 20, 21, 22–23, 24.
Janet Mager:
Pages 6–7, 8–9, 10, 26, 29, 30.
Leland Neff:
Pages 89, 91, 92, 122, 124, 125, 127, 128.
Susan Reinhardt:
Pages 32–33, 34, 35, 36, 38, 75, 77.
Ellwood Smith:
Pages 12–13, 15, 16, 18, 41, 42–43, 44, 52–53, 55, 56,
58, 62, 108, 111, 112.

Several of these stories first appeared in *Scope*, *Sprint*, and *Action*, copyright © 1973, 1977 by Scholastic Magazines, Inc.

12 11 10 9 8 7 6 5 4 3 2   8 9/70 1 2 3/8
Printed in the U.S.A.   09

CONTENTS

THE WILD RIDE

by Robert Juhren

Tim stood with the sled at the top of the hill. It seemed ten times higher from the top. It was a dangerous hill. Some boys had dared him to go down it. They said he would be afraid to try. They were now waiting at the bottom. They looked like small, dark spots on the snow below.

Tim wished he had not said anything. He told the boys he had raced down hills just like this one. Only Tim knew it was not true. Only he knew he had never been on a sled before. Never.

Tim's family had just moved north. They used to live in the South. Tim had never even seen snow before. But now he was in a new town. He had no friends. He felt he had to do something to make them.

The boys were waving now. He had put it off too long. He had to start down. He pulled the sled to the edge. He lay face down. He had seen the others do it. He

put his hands on the steering bar. Then
he put his feet in the snow behind him.
He looked down at the big tree at the
bottom of the hill they had told him about.
It was very cold on the hill. Tim wondered
why he was so hot.

He gave a push with his feet. He started
down the hill. The sled began to move.
Flying snow bit into his face. The wind
was roaring in his ears. Some of the hill
was covered with ice. The sled went faster.

All at once the sled went over a rock. Tim had not seen it. It had been covered by the snow. Tim fell half off. His knee hurt where he had hit the rock. Tim pulled himself back on. Soon the sled was going fast again. Tim looked. He was only half of the way down!

Snow and ice were still flying in his face. Tim saw a dark line across the hill. When he reached it, he saw it was a ledge. It was too late to do anything. The sled left the ground. It sailed into the air. Tim was holding on with all his might. He stayed on. He and the sled came down hard. Tim heard a noise. Then his arm hurt. Part of the sled had broken. The wood pressed against his arm. But the sled still kept moving.

Tim was almost at the bottom now. He just wanted to get there and get off. He tried not to think about his arm. He looked up. He forgot about his arm. The big tree was in his way. He was heading right for it. If he ran into it going this fast . . .

He closed his eyes. He pulled hard on the bar. He put both feet down. The sled turned too fast. His body kept going straight. He felt himself rolling. His hat was gone. His hair, face, and neck were covered with snow. He stopped rolling. He did not get up. He just lay there. The boys came running. They asked if he was all right.

Tim sat up. He hurt all over. He was tired. Then he saw the boys' faces. All at once he felt better. They were smiling.

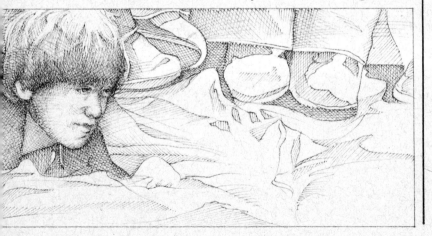

"Wow!" one of them said. "You sure can ride a sled."

"We didn't think you would do it," another one said. "Come on. We can all go to my house. My mother will fix us something warm."

They all started off together. Tim felt happy. He had done it. "But wow," he thought. "I sure won't brag again. At least not until I have really done it."

I DON'T LIKE YOUR FACE

by Juan Leon

Today is the big day. Today I am going to fight Tim Maloney. I don't really want to, but I think I am going to have to.

Tim Maloney is our school bully. Every school has its bully, so you know what kind of kid he is. He is just always looking for trouble. If you happen to be in his way, and you are doing something he doesn't like, he is going to give you trouble. It doesn't matter what you are doing.

It all began yesterday. It started out like any other day. When lunchtime came I went down to the lunchroom and got on line. We were waiting for the doors to open. Tim Maloney didn't want to wait.

"What's holding up those doors?" he yelled.

I was just standing on line waiting. Just standing there! But wouldn't you know it, Maloney decided to pick on me.

"I'm getting in front of you," he said. He looked me straight in the eye. It was my turn to say something. Everyone was waiting. "I don't like your face," he added.

I didn't think it was worth getting in trouble with him. He could be pretty mean. So I said, "You may get in front of me." I guess it was the wrong thing to say.

"I what!" he said. "I *may* get in front of you?" His face turned red. Somebody let out a little laugh. He didn't like that.

"Who thinks it's funny?" he asked.

No one said anything.

Just then the doors opened. Everything would have been fine if it wasn't for the pushing. I was pushed right into him. That did it.

"You want your nose pushed in?" he said. "I am going to..." Mr. Homes was walking by. Tim waited until he had passed. Then he said, "I better not find you on line tomorrow...or else." With that he went into the lunchroom.

I was pretty scared. My friend Jim asked me if I was going to tell a teacher.

"No," I said. "That would only make things worse." All I could do was wait until tomorrow and see. I didn't know what I was going to do.

Well, today is the big day. It is almost lunchtime.

"What are you going to do?" asked Jim.

14

15

16

"I'm going to get on line," I said. "No, wait a second. I'm going to wait until the line goes in. Then I won't have to worry about Tim." It sounded like a good idea. So I waited until I was sure the doors would be open. Then I went down. But wouldn't you know it? Tim was there waiting for me.

"I didn't think you were going to show," he said with a smile. "You can't be too smart," he added.

"There is no line, Tim," I said. "You said you had better not find me on line."

"For not being too smart," he said, "you have got a smart mouth. I don't want you coming down here at all!"

Well, it was getting to be too much. Bully or not, I was not going to go hungry or hide. Jim must have seen that look in my eye, because he was pulling my arm.

"Let go of my arm, Jim." I was getting angry. "You listen to me, Maloney," I said. That surprised him. "You had better lay off." This is it, I thought.

"OK," he said. He took a step toward me. He raised his hands, slowly. I took a deep breath, and then I raised my hands. That really surprised him.

17

"Uh...I'm going to let you off this time. But..."

"But nothing," I said. I knew he was backing out. Jim had a smile on his face.

Maloney put his hands back down and started to walk away.

"And *I* don't like *your* face," I called after him. He disappeared into the lunchroom.

During lunch, Jim told everyone what happened.

"You should have seen her," he said. "Kate really showed him!"

18

THE HARDEST JOB

by Nancy White

"Baby-sitting is easy," I told Fran. "All you do is put the child to bed. Then you watch TV." Some work!

Now cutting the grass *is* hard. First, you have to cut it. Then you have to cut the grass around the edges of the walk and rocks. You rake all the grass up. Then you bag it. And let me tell you, there is a lot of grass outside. So you can see it is more work than babysitting.

"All right," said Fran. "The next time I get a call, I will say I'm busy. I will ask if my brother can sit instead. Then we will see who works harder."

That night Fran got a call. It was from some new people down the street. I heard her say, "I'm busy Mrs. Winters. Can you use my brother?"

So the next night, there I was.

"Amy may stay up until 7:30," said Mrs. Winters. I saw Amy already had her night clothes on. That was one less thing to do.

"Can we play horsey?" asked Amy as soon as the Winters left. "You get down on the floor. Then I can ride you."

"I do not want to play that game," I said.

Tears came to Amy's eyes. "You better," she yelled. "Or I will tell Mother and Father you made me cry."

Well, I did not want any bad news getting back to Fran. She would laugh and say, "I told you so." So I played. I had to go around the house four times. Amy kept kicking and yelling, "Faster!" At last she got off.

"Now we can play hide and seek," she ordered. "I will hide. You can look for me."

I looked all over the house. I could not find her. Finally I looked in the bathroom. I pulled back the shower curtain. Before I knew it, I was all wet. Amy had turned on the water!

I dried off as best I could. Then I said, "Time for bed."

"Just one more game," Amy cried.

"All right. One more. Then you go straight to bed."

"We will play policeman," said Amy. "You can be the bad man. I will arrest you. Now put your hands behind your back."

Amy put toy handcuffs on me. But these had a real lock. And Amy had the key!

"Take these off right now!" I yelled.

"Now I can do anything I want," said Amy. "And you can't stop me." She turned on the TV. She sat down to watch. She had no thought of going to bed.

Then I got a bright idea. I pretended to hear something outside.

"Did you hear that?" I said. "It might be a burglar. Quick! Take these handcuffs off me."

Amy was afraid. She took off the handcuffs. She hid behind me. Then she saw I had tricked her. Boy, was she angry.

"Now I will never go to bed!"

I reached out for her. She ran out of the room. I looked all over the house for her. At last I looked in the Winters' closet. I found Amy on the floor, sleeping. I picked her up. I was very careful. I carried her into her room. I put her to bed. Soon after, the Winters' car pulled up.

"How did it go?" asked Mrs. Winters.

"Everything went just fine," I lied.

"It did?" said Mr. Winters. He looked surprised. "You are the first one who has been able to handle Amy. Can you come tomorrow afternoon?"

"I have to cut the grass tomorrow," I told him. "But maybe you can use my sister."

HIGH DIVE

by Les Purificación

Jim was always doing daring things. But no one thought Jim would try this. Not even me, and I'm his best friend. I thought I really knew him. But I guess I didn't. Best friends are not usually wrong about each other. But I sure was. Because there he was, a hundred feet above us. And all because of me.

The water seemed a cold gray. I wondered what it looked like from up

there. Sure I had looked down from the cliff before. But I never had to look at it the way Jim had to. He had to wait for when the water was just right. He had to wait for when the tide was at its highest.

When it was coming in, it would be too soon. When it was going out, it would be too late. I knew that Jim would have to catch it just right. There was no room for mistakes. He had been up there for a few minutes already.

The water hitting the rocks at the bottom of the cliff made little white circles. We were all standing very still and quiet. I don't know if I imagined it or if the sound of the water against the rocks was really getting louder. My neck was getting tired from looking up. But I wondered how *he* felt.

"Maybe he's not going to do it," someone said. I was about to say something. But some sea birds began screaming and flying up and down. Then it got quiet again. I didn't say anything.

I looked up at Jim. I felt a hard lump in my stomach. My head felt light. But I kept my eyes on him. It seemed like a long time. The water hitting the rocks was very loud in my ears now. I felt as if he was just about to dive. My mind raced. Then suddenly I knew it was all wrong. I opened my mouth but no words would come out. I swallowed hard.

"No Jim, don't do it!" The words came rushing out. I screamed again. "NO!"

I saw Jim looking down at me. It was a stupid dare. I should never have said anything. He was my best friend. I didn't want to lose him. "Jim, NO!"

He looked down at me. He didn't move. I started to run up the side of the cliff. But he waved his arm back and forth. He must have understood. He knew I didn't want him to do it.

For a minute I looked at him. But then suddenly he raised both his arms. He was going to jump! I saw him lean. His legs bent, and then he was off the cliff.

I saw him fall. I knew he had to clear the rocks and go in hands first. I held my breath. I could not move. Then I saw him hit the water. I ran down to the water's edge.

Our eyes were watching the spot where he had gone under. Then we saw him. His head and arms popped out of the water. He began to swim toward us. He looked OK. When he reached the shore we helped him out.

"Jim, didn't you hear me? You didn't have to jump," I said.

"I heard you," he said. "And thanks. I know you didn't want me to get hurt. But you know me, I had to do it."

I was a little surprised that he had said that. I really didn't think he would do it.

"Jim," I said. "Let's just say that I know you better now."

"Sure," he said. "But I know you pretty well. I know you will do it. It's your turn now."

THE JOKER

by Madeline Sunshine

"Hello!" said the voice on the other end of the telephone. "Is this Janet O'Malley?"

"Yes, it is," answered Janet. "Who is this?"

"Well you are a lucky girl, Janet. This is Rocking Rick Rufus and you are on Telephone Dollars. Do you know how to play?"

"I'm not sure," Janet answered.

"It's easy," said the voice. "If you can fill

in the lines in the song we will play, you win 50 dollars!"

Janet could hardly believe her ears. Just then she heard the music to *Old MacDonald Had A Farm*. As the name of each animal came on Janet made its sound. She oinked and moo'd and baa'd. But before she could cock-a-doodle-doo, she heard voices and loud laughing. One of the voices sounded all too familiar. Suddenly she knew exactly what was happening.

"Mike," she yelled. "I'm going to get you back for this. You and your bad jokes!" With that Janet banged down the telephone. "Boy," she thought, "all his friends were there laughing."

The next day, Janet waited for Mike in front of the school. Finally he showed up a minute before the bell.

"Hello," Janet called. "Can I talk to you a minute?"

"Sure," Mike said. He looked out of the corner of his eye.

"It's about what I said about getting you back. I tried to think of something to play on you, but I couldn't. So, let's forget it, OK?"

"Sounds OK to me," Mike said.

Just then the bell rang. They started walking into the building.

"Want some gum?" Janet asked.

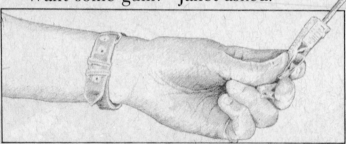

"That your last piece?" Mike asked.

"Yes, why?" Janet said.

"If it is your last piece there must be something wrong with it." Mike was not going to take any chances.

"OK," Janet said. She popped the gum into her mouth. "See, nothing wrong with it."

Mike just turned and walked into class.

A minute later, Janet walked into the room. She went over to Mike's desk.

"I just bumped into your brother," she said. "He wants you to meet him by the lunchroom. He said he has your lunch money."

"Very funny," Mike said. "That's not going to get me. He can't have my money because it's right..." Mike felt his pocket. "My lunch money—it's gone!"

"I told you," Janet said. She smiled as Mike ran out the door toward the lunchroom.

Mike could not wait for the day to be over. On the way home he thought that

tomorrow would have to be better. Maybe he would play another joke on Janet.

When he got home the telephone was ringing.

"Hello," he said.

"Mike, this is Mrs. Ames." Mrs. Ames was Mike's teacher. "I'm calling to ask you to do something for me."

"Sure," Mike said. "What is it?"

"Well," she said. "I'm having a birthday party for my little girl. I thought it would be fun to have you play some games with the kids. You have such a good sense of humor."

"Thank you, Mrs. Ames," Mike said. "I'll be glad to help you out."

"Also," she added. "Would you mind dressing up like a clown? The kids would really love that."

"That sounds great to me, Mrs. Ames," Mike said. "When should I be there?"

"Can you be here in about an hour?" she asked. "The house is at 514 Clarke Street."

"I'll be there," he said hanging up the telephone. "A good sense of humor," Mike thought to himself. "This is turning out to be a good day after all."

He borrowed his mother's make-up and painted his nose red and his face white. Then he painted on a big red smile. He felt funny walking down the street, but soon he was in front of 514 Clarke Street. He rang the bell and waited.

"Come in," called a voice from inside. He pushed the door open. Suddenly there was a bright flash. Then he heard loud laughing. When the white spots in front of his eyes disappeared, he looked around. In the middle of the room were Janet and half the girls from his class.

"Here," Janet said. "This is for you." She handed him an instant picture. "The next time you think of a joke, take a good look at yourself first and have a good laugh!"

"Boy, did she get me," Mike thought.

23-A

by George Shea

"So you want to be a paper boy?" the man said. He smiled. "Well, we *do* have a route open. It's number 23-A." He kept on smiling. But I didn't see anything funny.

"What is so funny?" I asked. "What is so special about 23-A?"

"You will see," he said.

"You will see," said a kid in the office.

"We start a *lot* of kids on that one," the man said.

"That's the one with the old lady and the dog," said the kid.

"That's the one all right," the man said. And he and the kid began to laugh.

23-A was a short route. I started the next day. I remembered what they said about the woman and her dog.

The dog was behind the gate of the 17th house on the route.

Big house.

Big dog. Very big. Very mean. Or so he seemed.

The house had a front lawn half the size of a football field. I was a good 50 yards from the gate to the house — too far to *throw* a paper. But maybe not too far to *run* — if I could run faster than the dog.

I thought of quitting right then and there. But I had a plan. "I'll get him away with some food," I thought. I reached into my pocket and pulled out my lunch. I threw it over the fence as far from me — and the house — as I could.

He went right for it. I went right for the house. And then he went right for me.

He knocked me over with a 20-foot leap. All my papers went flying. "This is IT!" I thought. "I'm going to DIE!"

But I didn't die. He started licking my face. He was sitting on my chest getting my face all wet. Then he started eating my papers. I tried to save as many as I could.

Just then, a woman came out. "Oh, Fido!" she yelled. "Bad dog. Bad dog." Fido got off of me.

"Here is your paper," I said to her. I handed her some wet papers.

"Thank you," she said. "You know, you are the 5th new paper boy this week."

I wanted to say something. But I was running back down the lawn after Fido. Fido had the front wheel of my bicycle in his mouth. He was pulling the whole bike

in through the open gate. Once he got it
inside, I knew he would try to eat as much
of it as he could. By the time I got it away
from him, half the seat was gone.

Later on, I went back to the office.

"How did it go?" asked the man with a
smile.

"Not so good," I said.

He gave me a long look. "Listen," he
said. "You want to try it again tomorrow?"

"I — I guess so," I said.

"That's good," he said. "You know, you
really can't make much money working
23-A. The dog eats too many of your
papers."

"Well," I said, "why don't you tell the lady to go to the store for her paper?"

"Because she owns the paper," he said. "But don't worry," he added. "As soon as another route opens up, you will get it. We always try kids out on 23-A. A lot of them leave after the first day. It's the ones who don't quit who make the best paper kids."

That was six months ago. I have got another route now. It's going OK.

A new kid just walked into the office. The man told him he could start with 23-A. I was standing next to the man's desk when he said it. I started to laugh. The kid turned to me.

"What is so funny?" he asked. "What is so special about 23-A?"

"You will see," I said.

BROTHERS

by Madeline Sunshine

It was snowing again. Mark stood in front of his window and watched the snow falling. He was thinking about the other times it had snowed.

"Mark," his mother called breaking into his thoughts. "Are you going out?"

Mark knew what *that* question meant. "Yes," he called, "I'm going out."

"Well then, take your brother David with you. And make sure he is wearing

socks. He sometimes forgets, you know."

Mark knew only too well. He waited a moment, and then he went into his brother's room. David was sitting on the floor, holding his catcher's mitt.

"We going out, Mark? We going outside?" David asked.

"Yes, we are going out," Mark said. He didn't sound very happy. "Let's get your socks on, OK?"

"My red ones? I like my red ones."

"Boy," Mark thought to himself as he helped his brother put on his socks. "Why do I always have to take him? What kind of older brother is he? Why can't he be just like other people?" Mark looked at his brother angrily. But David just smiled and held tight to his mitt.

Outside the wind blew snow in their faces as they made their way toward the park. Some boys were having a snowball fight. When they saw Mark and David they stopped.

"Oh, it's you," yelled one of the boys.

"Hello," called Mark.

"What did you have to bring him for?" asked another boy, pointing at David.

"He's my brother," Mark answered.

47

"He's a dummy," called another boy. Then things started happening very fast. Another boy yelled, "Let's get the dummy!" A boy tried to take David's mitt while the others hit him with snow. David began to run, falling as he ran.

For a moment Mark just stood there. He tried to forget that David was his brother and that he had to take care of him. "Good," he thought. "Go on, run. Maybe now I can have some fun. Maybe . . ."

The other boys were still laughing. Mark heard them yell, "He's running away. Look at the dummy go!"

Suddenly Mark yelled, "Shut up! He's not a dummy. He's retarded. That's different."

"It is not," said one of the boys.

"It is, it is," Mark yelled. "He can't help it. He was born that way. But you, why do you all have to make fun of him? I think you are mean and . . ." Mark didn't finish the sentence. He thought of his brother, off all by himself and afraid. Then he began to run as fast as he could. He didn't stop until he found his brother.

David was sitting knee-deep in snow, his mitt lying beside him.

"David, are you OK?" Mark asked catching his breath. "What are you doing?"

"Just sitting," David answered smiling at his brother.

"Just sitting?" Mark said. "In the snow?" He looked at his brother and took a deep breath. "Come on David. You are getting all wet. Let's go home now." David did not move. "I'll make you a sandwich if you want," Mark added.

"With everything on it?" asked his brother, his face lighting up.

"With everything on it," answered Mark. David stood up and Mark put his arm around him.

"I'm glad you came," David said. "I was cold."

"Yes, I know," Mark said. Deep inside, Mark still wished he had a brother who would put his arm around him. But he smiled as he looked at the spot where David was sitting. He noticed David's mitt still lying there, waiting to be picked up. He grabbed it, dusted the snow off, and gave it to his brother. Then the two of them started home.

THE NIGHT BROTHER SMITH CAME BACK

by Ray Shepard

I was in the 6th grade when my great-grandfather died. He was 89 and I was 12. I didn't know him very well. But my mother and father still took me to the funeral. I had never been to one before. I don't think I will ever go again.

My grandmother and her father lived a long way from us. It took us five hours to drive there.

My great-grandfather was called Brother

Smith. I don't know why. I think he must have been a little strange. I heard my grandmother say he used to get up in the middle of the night to put on after-shave lotion.

My great-grandfather had a cat named Hugo. Hugo was strange too. I don't like cats much. I think Hugo knew that. He was always looking at me. He would follow me from room to room. It was like he was making sure I didn't do anything wrong.

The funeral was held in a large church.

53

My great-grandfather had belonged to that church all his life. The funeral was not so bad. There was a lot of talking and singing. At the end, people got up and walked to the front of the church. They all wanted to see Brother Smith for the last time. I had only seen him a few times when he was alive. I didn't want to see him now that he was dead.

It was what happened *after* the funeral that made me sure I would never go to another one.

There was a dinner. No one seemed too sad about Brother Smith being gone. Some friends said they would miss him. Dad said he had lived a good life. Grandmother said dying was a part of living. Mother said she hoped she lived to be 89.

We had to spend the night. My grandmother's house was small. There were not many beds. In the living room there was a small pull-out bed. Mom and Dad got that. I had to sleep in Brother Smith's room.

I asked Dad if I could sleep in the car. He laughed. He wanted to know if I was afraid. I told him, "Of course not." But of course I was.

That night I stayed up as long as I could. It was almost one in the morning before Dad made me go to bed.

There was only a bed and a table in my great-grandfather's room. The table was covered with after-shave bottles. Hugo followed me into the room. I don't think he liked the idea of my being there.

I tried to go to sleep, but I just could not. I lay there in the dark. I could see Hugo's large, yellow eyes. They never closed. At some point I must have gone to sleep. Later, I suddenly woke up. Brother Smith was standing by the bed. He was wearing the same clothes he had on at the funeral. I could smell after-shave all over him.

"Did I wake you?" he asked.

What do you say to a person whose funeral you have just gone to? So I said nothing.

"It's a soft bed, right?" he asked after a while.

I shook my head yes. I was not about to disagree with him.

"Well, I've had a long day," he said. "Funerals always make me tired. I need some sleep."

I started shaking my head no while he was talking.

"Yes," he said. "I need some sleep. I have got a big day tomorrow."

It was at that point I knew I was screaming. I was also trying to run. Running in bed is not easy!

The bed must have been old. My running was too much for it. It broke. Hugo was under the bed. He started screaming when the bed landed on him. Our screaming brought my grandmother and my mother and father into the room. They said I was just dreaming. I knew better. The tops were off all the bottles, and I could still smell the after-shave.

NO TROUBLE AT ALL

by William Stine

I knew there was going to be trouble the first time I saw him. It was something about the way that cowboy rode into town. He sat backward on his horse. I figured right then he was a strange one, and he looked real mean.

He rode across the street. He rode over to my office. Then he rode right through my door. He wrecked my whole door.

"Are you the Sheriff?" he growled.

"What is the matter with you?" I asked. "Don't you know better than to ride your horse into my office without knocking first?"

"Sorry," he said. "I'll knock next time." But I don't think he meant it because just then he began to laugh. It was a strange laugh. It sounded just like a turkey, but then I knew who he was. He was the outlaw: Billy the Bully.

"What are you doing in my town?" I asked.

"I got something important to do," he said. Then he laughed again.

"You think that you are pretty mean, don't you?" I said.

"Sheriff," he said. "Mean *is* my middle name."

"Really," I said. "Mine is Ronald. I was named after my grandfather. He ..." Billy didn't let me finish.

"After I'm through, your name is going to be mud," he said. Then he laughed like a turkey again. "You got a place I can stay in this fleabag town?" he asked.

"Yes," I said. "It's called the Fleabag Hotel. It's at the end of the street. You can't miss it."

He turned his horse around and rode out of my office. He didn't even close the door, but I didn't mind. I didn't have a door to close now.

I watched him ride down the street. Then I watched him ride right through the doors of the hotel. I knew it was only a matter of time now. The trouble would start soon.

The next morning, Mabel came into my office. Mabel runs the Fleabag Hotel.

"Good morning, Mabel," I said.

"What is so good about it, Sheriff?" she said.

Something about her answer made me think she was angry.

"Sheriff, you have got to arrest Billy the Bully. If you don't there will be trouble."

"I can't arrest a man for riding into town backward," I said.

"Do you know what he did this morning?" Mabel yelled. "He brought his horse into my kitchen. Right into my kitchen! Then he ordered beans and eggs and a pail of oats. He gave the beans and eggs to his horse. Then *he* ate the oats!"

"Can't arrest a man for not eating your cooking, Mabel. In fact, he might be smarter than I thought."

Now Mabel was really angry.

"Sheriff," she said. "I came here for help and you sit there and make jokes." With that she walked out of my office.

Just then I heard shooting out on the street. I ran out of my office. Forgetful Fred ran up to me. They call him that because he can never remember anything.

"What is all the shooting?" I asked.

"What shooting?" asked Forgetful. "Wait, I remember! It's Billy the Bully. You have got to arrest him."

"What for!" I asked.

"He is trying to hold up the bank," said Forgetful.

61

"I can't arrest him for holding up the bank," I said.

"You can't? Why not?" asked Forgetful.

"Because we don't have a bank in this town," I said.

"I forgot," said Forgetful.

Then I saw Billy the Bully. He was coming across the street, and he looked angry.

"What is the idea of hiding the bank!" he yelled. "Where is it?"

"We don't have a bank," I told him.

"Sure you do. This is Dry Gulch and I have been planning to rob the Dry Gulch Bank since last week," Billy said.

"Well, sorry to disappoint you. This is Dry Throat," I said. "Dry Gulch is 20 miles south of here."

"Guess I made a mistake," Billy said. Then he laughed that turkey laugh.

"Well, can't arrest a man for making a mistake," I said.

After that, he got on his horse.

"Dry Gulch is that way," I pointed. Then he rode out of town. But Billy was riding backward, so his horse was going the wrong way.

"Well, Forgetful—looks like I was wrong. He was not going to make trouble after all."

"Who?" asked Forgetful.

GEORGE'S RAFT

by Les Purificacion

"George ... George Taylor! What are you doing?"

George turned and looked at his sister Judy. "How did she find me?" George thought. This was supposed to be one of his best kept secrets. He tried to look cool. He was not going to let his sister get in the way, not this time.

"George Taylor, I'm talking to you. What are you doing with those old tires?" She

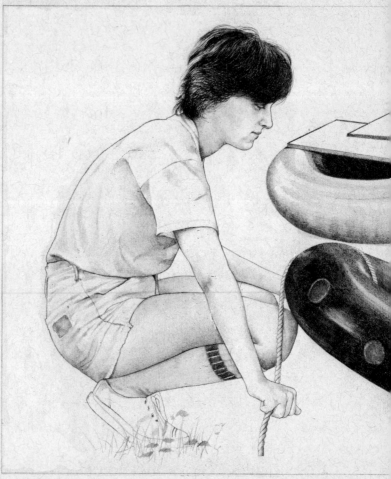

stood there with that look on her face. George knew that once Judy got on to something she was harder to shake than an angry bee.

"Well, if you must know," George said. "I'm building a raft."

"A what!" Judy said. "Wait a minute,

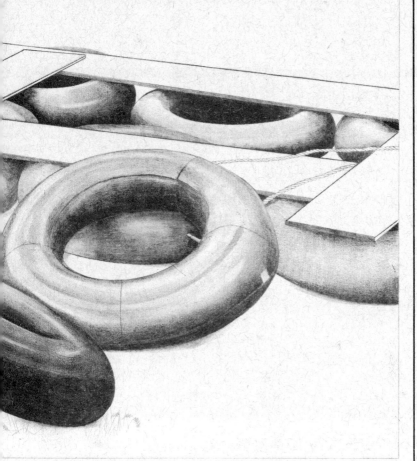

George. You are not planning to ..."

"That's right," George said. "I'm taking it over the Silver River rapids. Just one more tire and I'm ready to go!"

"I'll tell you where you are going, George," Judy snapped. "You are going home, right now!"

"Oh, oh," George thought. He couldn't let his plans end so fast. The raft was almost ready.

"Come on, Judy," George said. "I was only joking. I'm building it so we can have some fun at the swimming hole. Come on.

Help me get it down to the river bank."

Judy looked at him hard. But then she smiled. "OK, George. I would like to go for a swim, but the rapids are out. OK?"

"OK," George said. "But there was still

tomorrow," he thought.

The river ran lower and slower during the summer. That was why George thought it was the best time to try the rapids. Judy was really a great sister, but sometimes she just did not understand.

When they got to the river Judy said, "George, if we put the raft out it will be carried away." Near the bank, the water ran a lot slower than in the middle. But George had an idea.

"We can tie it with this rope to the swing tree," he said. He pointed to the tree that hung over the swimming hole. "It will float out a little, but the rope will hold it."

The rope was about 10 feet long. George tied one end to the raft. Then he tied the other end to the tree. The raft floated out to the end of the rope.

"You see," George said. Then he jumped in and swam out to the raft. "It's great," he called.

Judy was about to jump in. But just then the rope snapped. The pull of the river and George's weight must have been too much.

"George!" Judy yelled. The raft had begun to move away toward the middle of the river. "Jump off, George! Jump off!" she called.

"Quick, grab the end of the rope!" George called. He did not want to lose his raft.

There was no time to argue with him. The end of the rope was still within reach. Judy jumped in quickly and grabbed it. She pulled with all her might, but the raft just pulled her along. She tried to swim toward the river bank, but the more she tried, the more tired she got.

"George," she called. "I can't do it. We are moving too fast." They both knew that now they were being pulled by the rapids. "Oh, no," George thought. He could see the bend just before the rapids.

"Judy," he called. "The water slows down at the bend. You can swim to the side there." The raft had already begun to move out to the far side of the river, where the water was fastest. It would not matter now if he tried to swim. He would be pulled through the rapids. They had reached the bend.

"Let go!" George yelled. He was sorry that he had ever had the idea. But Judy held on. She was on the slower side and the water was not as hard against her. She

was trying for a tree that was sticking out from the bank. Just a little more ... She reached out.

"George, I got it!" she yelled. She had one arm around the tree and the other on the rope. But how long could she hold on? The water was still pulling the raft.

Suddenly the raft began falling apart. Judy screamed as she saw George go under. The tires went rushing away. But just then George came up. He had held on to the rope!

It was a lot easier to hold on now. "Pull yourself toward me," Judy said. Soon George had pulled himself to the tree. In another minute, they were both out of the water and safe.

They both sat on the bank taking deep breaths. George decided that going over the rapids was one thing he did not want to do anymore. And this was one time he was sure glad his sister *did* get in the way.

HOGBALL HARRY

by Herb and Mary Montgomery

"Pass it to me!" TJ yelled. He was the Wildcats' center. There wasn't a Trotter within 10 feet of him. TJ waved his arms up and down. "Over here, Harry!" Harry looked at TJ but dribbled on without passing.

"Hogball!" TJ said. "Hogball Harry!"

Harry paid no attention. He went right, then he went left and around the man on him. He made the Trotters look like their feet were tied together. TJ liked being on the winning team, but Harry made the others feel like they were just taking up space. The coach didn't seem to mind as long as they kept winning.

TJ watched Harry go around the last Trotter. Then Harry made a quick turn and shot. The ball went clean in. The Wildcats had the lead.

They held the lead until the second half. Then it happened. A Trotter threw a long shot up. It missed, but as Harry went for the ball he jammed his fingers. Harry was out of the game, and the Wildcats lost. To top it off, Harry would be out for at least three weeks. Without Harry the team would be called the "Kitty Cats."

There seemed to be no hope for the team now. But TJ liked basketball so much that he kept playing. He put in more practice. The rest of the team did too. When it was time to play again, one of the boys said, "We will never win without Harry."

"We can try," TJ said. Then the game began. TJ jumped and tipped the ball to a forward. He passed off to Little Eddie who raced in for two points.

The Wildcats were surprised. The coach was surprised too. "Great play," he yelled.

There was a lot of good playing that game. Every Wildcat made some points, and they almost won. TJ could not believe it. They were playing like a team.

Harry was back the next week. Before the game he bragged, "You *all* look almost as good as I do." TJ and the others just winked behind Harry's back and laughed.

The game began. The Rockets got the jump and the first four points of the game. Harry's face was red. He hated to lose. He yelled at TJ, "Give me the ball!" TJ looked at Harry but passed the ball to Little Eddie.

"Stop hogging the ball!" Harry ordered.

The Rockets got the ball and made another two points. When the Wildcats passed in the ball, Harry took it from his own man. He ran for the basket. The whistle blew, but Harry went in for a lay-up. It went in but didn't count. He was called for walking.

At the end of the half, the team sat around the coach. Harry complained. "We are going to lose again. You guys are hogging the ball...." Harry was angry.

"You guys are doing it on purpose!"

TJ didn't laugh. Harry seemed angry enough to bite through a telephone pole.

The coach said, "Practice has made the whole team better, Harry. We can't win with one star player." The coach turned to the others and said, "The four of you can't win by playing hogball. You know that."

The whistle sounded for the second half. "Work together, team!" the coach called.

TJ waited for the jump. He wondered if he should tip the ball to Harry. He didn't want to. But when the ball went up, TJ knew what he had to do. He jumped high and tipped the ball to Harry. Harry was so surprised that he almost lost it. Then he went toward the basket like a runaway train.

Hogging the ball again! TJ thought angrily. But suddenly Harry changed direction. He dribbled to the side and stopped. Then he passed the ball to another man.

"Slow it down," Harry called.

The other Wildcats looked very surprised as they ran to set up a play. They passed the ball around quickly. The Rockets were running around trying to get the ball. Little Eddie got into the open and put in a short jump shot.

The Wildcats were really moving! "We are a team," TJ thought as he ran, "and no one has to play hogball." As he looked around at the rest of the team, he had a good feeling. He was sure that together the Wildcats would win again.

FLASH FLOOD

by Herb and Mary Montgomery

Rain splashed on the window. It was dark outside. I jumped as lightning flashed. The rain fell harder. Where were Mom and Dad? They should have been home by now. I was worried. No one expected it to rain so hard.

Our telephone rang. It was Mom. "We can't get home, Sara," she said. "The rain has come down so fast that the river is going to flashflood. We were stopped at

the bridge. The road is already flooded."

I tried to keep my hands from shaking. "What will Jerry and I do?" I asked.

"Be brave and do what I tell you," she said. "Soon a big wall of water will come down the river. Take Jerry and run up the hill behind the house. You will be safe there."

"I can't..." I said as something went wrong with the telephone. "Mom!" I yelled. She didn't answer. Suddenly the lights went out.

The house was dark. I found my way to the kitchen. I found the flashlight, and then I went to wake up my brother, Jerry. He can sleep through anything. I shook him hard. "Wake up," I called. "A flood is coming!"

Jerry is only six, but we live by a river and he knows what a flood is. I told him about Mom's call. Dad had been on a trip and Mom had gone to town to pick him up. The road to town goes along the river and over the bridge to high ground. "Mom and Dad are safe at the bridge," I said. "But we have to get to a higher place."

Jerry and I pulled on our coats. Then we stepped out into the black night.

"What is that noise?" Jerry asked.

"Rain," I said. It pounded down all around us. I took Jerry's hand and moved toward the hill.

"Look!" Jerry yelled. "There is a *new* river!"

He was right. The river flooded across our yard. Now there was no way to get to the hill behind our house.

"What are we going to do, Sara?" Jerry asked. Then he started to cry.

"We will find a safe place, Jerry," I promised.

"But where could we go?" I wondered. There were no tall trees to climb. There was no way to get away from the water. It was getting deeper and deeper. I had never felt so scared, but I could not let Jerry know that.

Then I thought about getting up on a roof. The house roof was too steep. But we could get up on the garage.

Jerry helped me pull out the ladder and put it up. But then he didn't want to go up on the roof. "It's the only safe place, Jerry," I said as I pushed him up the ladder.

We crawled to the very top. Lightning flashed, and everything looked strange. Water fell like rivers from the sky. The cold water ran down my neck. I put my arm around Jerry to keep him warm. We sat there waiting. Soon I heard a roar in the night. I knew the wall of water was coming! "Hang on to the edge!" I yelled.

Water hit against the garage. Water splashed over us. The garage shook. My feet slid, but I held on to Jerry and the roof. I felt the garage move and then it lifted right off the ground.

"We are moving!" Jerry cried.

"I know," I said. "But we are still safe."

"How long will we be safe?" I asked myself. "Will the garage go under? Or will we get pushed off when we come to the bridge?"

We floated and floated. I could not see anything in the dark. All of a sudden we hit something. I turned on the flashlight to see what it was. We had hit the bridge.

The river was so high that the garage could not go under it. The garage turned in the water. What if the garage starts to break up? What if we fall into the flooding river?

"We have got to get on the bridge, Jerry," I yelled. I pulled him along the roof. The water splashed around us.

"Keep going. Keep going," I kept saying. At last I stood up and felt the bridge railing. I pulled Jerry up beside me. Then I pushed him over. Then I went over.

The old bridge shook and I was sure it was going to break up. I took Jerry's hand and pulled him along. "Run!" I yelled.

And run we did. We ran all the way to the end of the bridge. A policeman had the bridge blocked with his car. He sure looked surprised to see us. After we told him what had happened, he said, "Come on, I'll help you find your parents."

Behind us, I heard boards snapping. I knew the garage was breaking up. I put my arm around Jerry as we went to find Mom and Dad. What a story we had to tell them.

LONG TOES

by Les Purificación

When I was small my father used to
scare me with stories about a monster. He
said it was half something and half
something else. He also said that it lived in
the woods behind our farm. He said they
called it Long Toes. Because, from its
footprints, they saw the thing had 12 long
toes.

Our farm was in a corner of the
Northwest. Around the farm the woods

stretched for miles. It was wild forest. No place for greenhorns, or little children.

When I was a little older I thought it was great having our own monster. I had heard the stories about Bigfoot, and here we had our very own Long Toes. My mother and father would say to me, "If you don't watch out, Bigfoot or Long Toes will get you." I would scream and run behind my mother's dress.

Now I was much older. And it had been some time since they had talked about Long Toes. I guess because I was getting too old to be scared by it. And I was old enough to know the dangers of the forest. But now there was real reason to be scared. I had found a set of tracks in my flower garden. And they could only have been made by one thing — Long Toes!

At first I thought it was a joke. But when I showed my father, he seemed surprised. And to top it off he went and got the sheriff.

"Yup, Jake," he said to my father. "These here tracks were made by something strange. Look like the ones I saw down Miller's Pond some years back. But they look a bit smaller."

I was angry. Most of my flowers were gone. But I must say, I was a little scared. The flower bed was just outside my window. About a hundred yards away, the forest edge began. I had not heard a thing. "Must be a quiet monster," I thought. "But pretty mean to tear up all my beautiful flowers like that." They were real pretty.

At least there were a few left.

That night my father stayed out on the steps to the house. He had a gun with him. But that night the thing didn't show up. Or the next night, or the next. Finally my father gave up watching. Farming is a hard life, and he needed all his rest. But I had not given up. I stayed up and watched from my window.

On the fourth night I was about to give up and go to bed. It was a dark night, because the moon was covered by clouds. So I guess that was why I didn't see it right away. Finally, I did see it. I hid behind the curtain. I was ready to yell, but then it moved toward me. It moved very quickly. Then I saw it look up. It was looking straight at my window. I could not move or yell. It waited for a second, then it moved closer. Its face was dark and I really didn't see it very well. But I could tell it had two arms, two legs, and a short, strong body. It had reached the flower bed.

I was about to scream when all of a sudden I saw it bend down. It started to dig around the flowers that were left. It was digging them out from the roots!

When it had the last flowers out, it put them carefully under its arm.

Just then I got brave enough to run to my father's room. I got him out of bed, and in his shorts he ran outside with the gun. But it was gone. We walked over to the flower bed and the rest of my flowers were gone too.

That year the monster did not come back. We did not find any more of its tracks on the farm or in the woods near the farm. But the following spring it showed up again.

I had been working all day on my garden, getting it ready so that I could plant my flower seeds. It was hard work and I had not finished by dark. I had decided to leave the planting until the next day. Later that night I remembered that I had left the seeds outside. If they were outside all night, they would not be any good. But when I got to the garden, I was in for a surprise. The flower seeds were gone. All that was left were tracks made by Long Toes.

My mother and father could not make any sense of it. It was the strangest thing. I could not make anything of it either, but that spring I planted a small vegetable garden and crossed my fingers.

CRAZY WILLIE

by Ray Shepard

His house was on the corner right down the street from me. He and his mother lived there alone for more than 30 years. It looked like any old kind of house. I mean, it had flowers and a fence all around. And his mother made him clean the front steps every day. But it was a strange house. I knew it because I lived on the same street. I knew it was Crazy Willie's house.

I had never done anything to him

before. I had to pass his house coming and going to school. Just as I would get near the house, Willie would come out with his broom and look at me. At first I was scared, and I would walk across the street. Willie would look at me until I was almost by. Then he would start sweeping as if he were angry. Or as if he were trying to hide in all the dust.

After a while I stopped being scared. I would walk across the street before I saw

him, but he would always be there watching me. Then when I was almost by, he would start sweeping up a storm.

That's how we got along. I didn't bother him, and he didn't bother me.

One day something happened. I didn't mean to do anything to him. It was the other kids who started it. They didn't live on the same street. So they didn't have to make their peace with Willie. All I did was tell them how crazy Willie acted.

One afternoon, when we were almost by his house, we stopped. And we yelled, "Crazy Willie! Crazy Willie's too dumb to do anything!" I could not help from yelling right along with them.

The next morning, when I was alone, I knew I should not have done it. I knew I should have kept my peace with him. I didn't want to go to school, but I had to. As soon as I left my house, I walked across the street. I went by Willie's house as fast as I could, but I could see he was not there.

That afternoon the kids came back and

started yelling in front of his house. I didn't because that morning had taught me something. I stayed on the other side of the street, watching.

"Crazy Willie!" they yelled. I could see Willie looking out a window and I hoped he could see that I was not with them.

The door opened slowly, and the yelling stopped. Willie came out and stood there with a pail. When they saw he wasn't going to do anything, they started yelling again.

Suddenly Willie came running off the front steps. Before anyone could move,

Willie was right up to the fence. And he threw the pail of water getting them all wet. Willie went back in his house shaking his head from side to side. I was glad I had stayed on the other side of the street.

After that I didn't see Willie. We had all stopped bothering him, but the other kids kept going home the same way. I guess they wanted to show they were not afraid of him. I was glad they did. I didn't like walking alone now.

One day our teacher got angry and kept us after school. We felt we had not done anything wrong. On the way home, we were talking about it loudly. No one was even thinking about Willie, but he must have thought all the noise was meant to bother him. One minute we were all walking easy and talking loudly. Then somebody yelled, "Here comes Crazy Willie!"

We all started running without even thinking. Willie was racing out of his house. I could see he didn't have a pail this time, so I stopped. But Willie jumped right over the fence and kept coming. I was the closest, and he came straight for me.

I tried to run. My legs were moving all right, but my feet kept getting in the way. Before I could get down the street, I felt Willie's hand on the back of my neck. At first I could not move. Then I turned around. His face was so close I could see little pieces of gray hair coming out of his face. His teeth were yellow, and his eyes were sad. Then I saw that he was crying.

"Why you?" he kept saying. "Why you?"

And I kept saying, "I didn't mean to. I didn't mean ..."

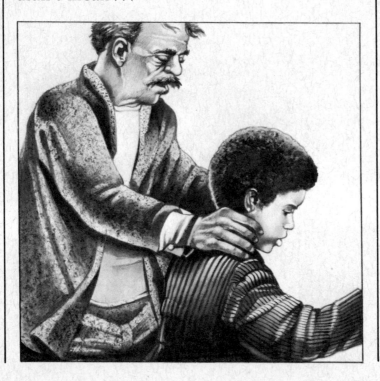

He must have believed me. Or maybe he thought it was wrong to cry in front of me. I don't know, but he turned and walked away.

His arms were just hanging down, and he shook his head from side to side. His walk was very slow. I wondered how he ever jumped that fence. I could tell by the way he walked that he was an old, lonely man.

Then I felt sorry that he had no one to talk to except his mother. And she had to be older and lonelier. I wanted to do something for him. I wanted to let him know I was really sorry I had hurt him. But what could I do? I could never go on the other side of that fence to talk to him.

YOU CAN COUNT ON A FRIEND

by Phyllis Landau

Donald and Tommy were waiting in the park for their friends. They were looking through some comic books they had found. Just then they heard the bells of the ice-cream man. Donald nudged Tommy.

"There's the ice-cream man," Donald said. "Let's buy some ice cream."

"OK," Tommy said. He pulled out 25 cents and handed it to Donald. "Here, get me a chocolate pop."

Donald looked at the money. "Hey, Tommy," he said slowly. "Could you lend me 25 cents? I don't have any money."

"You never have any money," Tommy said. But he reached into his pocket and pulled out another 25 cents.

Donald ran over to the ice-cream man. On his way back, Donald saw something in the grass. It was a wallet. It was a lucky day. First they found the comic books and now, a wallet!

"Tommy!" Donald called, "look what I found."

Tommy rushed over.

"Look, Tommy," Donald said. "There is 12 dollars in it!"

Tommy took the wallet and looked through it. He found a picture of a baby and a card with a name and address: Rita Bornstein, 10 Look Drive.

"The name of the owner is on this card," Tommy said. "We can return the wallet and maybe get a reward!"

Donald looked at Tommy. "What!" he said. "Finders keepers!"

"But maybe she needs the money," Tommy said. "And besides, it's not right."

"Listen," Donald said. "You get half the

money—six dollars! Now that's a lot of chocolate pops."

"It's stealing," Tommy said flatly.

"It's not stealing!" Donald said. He was getting angry. "She lost it and I found it—just like the comic books."

"Do what you want," Tommy finally said. "But I don't want anything."

Just then Andy, Rich, and Benny came into the park. They had a basketball and they were heading for the courts. "Come on!" they called to Tommy and Donald.

They passed the ball around and were taking shots. Tommy was about to shoot when he noticed a woman with a baby watching them.

"Can we help you?" called Benny.

"Perhaps," the woman said. "Did any of you boys find a wallet? I was in the park earlier today with Janie. I might have dropped it around here."

Tommy looked over at Donald. But Donald did not say anything.

"No, we didn't see any wallet," Benny said.

"Well, if you find it, my address is inside. There will be a reward," she said. Then she walked away.

Tommy felt sorry for the lady. He should have said something. He didn't say anything because Donald was his friend. Maybe he should have said something anyway. He knew Donald was wrong.

They played until it was almost dark. On the way home Tommy did not talk to Donald.

"Come on," Donald said. "Talk to me, will you?"

"I have nothing to say," Tommy said.

"You are making me feel bad," Donald said.

"The lady who lost the wallet feels bad, and so do I."

"You? Why should you feel bad? You didn't lose anything," Donald said.

"I feel bad because I didn't say anything," Tommy answered.

"You didn't say anything because you are a real friend," Donald said.

"That's just it," Tommy said. "Friends should not make each other feel bad."

Donald knew what Tommy meant. After a while Donald said, "Listen, Tommy, I'll return the wallet."

"I knew I could count on you." Tommy smiled and put his arm around Donald's back. His friend did not let him down.

Just then, they passed an ice-cream shop.

"Let's get a couple of chocolate pops," Donald said.

"Sure," Tommy smiled.

"There is just one thing," Donald added. "You are going to have to lend me another 25 cents."

NO MORE STUDYING

by Juan Leon

"I think this is the craziest idea you have ever had," said Phyllis. "Besides, Cora," she continued. "What makes you think it will work?"

Cora looked her machine over. It was finally finished. Three long months of saving and running all over town to get the parts.

"It will work," Cora answered. "When I told you about the idea three months ago you thought it was great. Well, now all we have to do is step inside and . . ."

"Wait a second, Cora, Phyllis said. "I

was just joking. Do you really think that
... that thing will work?"

"But don't you think it is worth it?"
Cora asked. "I mean ... If we knew what
was going to be on our tests before we had
to take them, then we would always do
great!"

"Forget it, Cora," her friend said. "All I
know is that you had better study for that
test next week. And cut out all this
daydreaming."

"Suit yourself," Cora said. "I just know
that I am never going to have to study
ever again."

With that Phyllis left and Cora was
alone with her machine. She pushed some
buttons and turned some knobs. Just then
she felt a little tired, but she stepped
inside and was gone. Cora landed right
outside the school building a week later.
All the kids were going inside, and they
didn't seem to see her.

"This is great," she said to herself. Then
she went to her classroom. Ms. Caraway
was there, and so were a lot of the kids.
Phyllis was there too. She didn't look very
happy. She was probably worried about
the test.

The class was still coming in. Cora decided to have a little fun. "I wonder if I can move things around," she thought. She walked over to her desk. Her desk was right next to Phyllis's. Phyllis was writing something. Cora reached for a book, but her hand went right through it! She tried to touch a chair, a desk, even Phyllis, but it was the same thing.

Cora walked over to the teacher's desk. Right on top were the test papers. "I'll never study again," Cora said to Ms. Caraway. But of course, she could not hear her. Cora looked the test over. "This will be easy," she thought.

Just then the bell rang. Cora almost went back to her seat, but then she remembered. She was not really there. At least not to them.

Ms. Caraway picked up the test papers and stood in front of her desk. Cora could tell everyone was waiting. But then Ms. Caraway put the test papers back down.

"We will not have the test today," she said. "I know how worried and upset we have all been since Cora disappeared...."

"What!" cried Cora. But of course, no one could hear her. "Disappeared? But

..." Then it hit her. How was she going to get back?

"Ms. Caraway, Ms. Caraway!" Cora screamed. "I'm here!"

"We will have the test some other time," Ms. Caraway continued.

"Oh, no," cried Cora. "What will happen to me?" She ran over to Phyllis's desk.

"Phyllis," she said, trying to touch her. But it was no use. Phyllis was busy writing. She did not even raise her head.

"Cora, Cora!" It was Ms. Caraway. Cora looked up from her desk. She was... "Time is up. Would you please pass down your test paper."

Phyllis looked at Cora. Phyllis knew that Cora had been daydreaming again.

THE BUS STOP GAME

by Madeline Sunshine

"Come on," said Neil. "I'm tired of playing."

"Just one more bus," said his sister, Laurie. "Please!"

"OK," said Neil. "But just one more."

Laurie loved the bus stop game. They would watch people hurry off each bus. Then they would try to guess what each person did. The man with the suit had to be a teacher. The woman with the red hair *had* to be a model. That was how the game went.

Neil didn't really want to play. He was watching the only other person at the bus stop — the Tall Lady. She had been there almost as long as they had. Every once in a while, she would smile at them. Laurie guessed she was a dancer. Neil thought she was rich and didn't have to work. They both thought she was beautiful. "She must be waiting for something," Neil thought. She was holding a suitcase.

Just then Laurie called out. "I see it, Neil! It's coming," she said.

Neil wondered if this time the Tall Lady would get on. But just as the bus pulled up, a car came from behind and screeched to a stop. The Tall Lady moved back surprised. The car door flew open and a big man jumped out. Suddenly the Tall Lady began to run. Laurie and Neil took off too. They were not going to wait to see what the man was going to do. The Tall Lady was just in front of them. She was having trouble running with the suitcase. They saw her throw it to the side.

"The suitcase, Laurie. Get it!" cried Neil. "We have got to help her."

115

The Tall Lady turned around but kept going. She disappeared in an alley down the street.

"Come on," yelled Neil.

"This thing is heavy," Laurie said. But then she looked back. Now the big man was chasing them.

"Stop you two," they heard him yell. "Why," they wondered, "was this man chasing the Tall Lady?" It had to be the suitcase. The Tall Lady had looked plenty scared. And now so were they.

Just then they turned into the alley, and there she was. She was resting against a wall. The Tall Lady looked very frightened.

"Quick," yelled Neil. "Duck into that building!" The Tall Lady ran toward it.

Laurie quickly looked behind her. Just then the man turned into the alley.

"Stop," he yelled. He was waving something in his hand.

"Neil!" screamed Laurie. "He has got a gun!" Now they had almost reached the building.

Laurie and Neil ran through the door. "Miss, Miss," called Neil. "It's us. We have got your suitcase." The Tall Lady peeked out from behind the door.

"That man!" said Laurie. "He has a gun!" The Tall Lady pulled the suitcase out of Laurie's hand.

"This way," said Neil. "We can go through the building." Then it happened. They heard a sound behind them. "Hurry!" cried Neil. "Lady, please hurry!" But it was too late.

"OK, hold it," yelled the man. "Drop that suitcase, Jenny." He walked over to the lady, still holding his gun. "Thought you could get away, didn't you," he said.

Just then they heard police sirens. "We are saved," thought Neil and Laurie. Four police officers came running into the building with their guns out.

"It's all right," said the man. "Everything is under control. Just handcuff her and get her out." Neil's and Laurie's mouths dropped open.

"I'm a policeman," the man said.

"But . . . but, the Tall Lady," said Neil.

"That lady just tried to pull off one of the biggest robberies of all time," the man

118

said. "And you two could have been hurt or killed. She is dangerous."

The man opened the suitcase. Inside were jewels. Laurie and Neil had never seen anything like it before.

"You two will have to come down to the station with me," said the policeman.

"Are we under arrest?" asked Neil.

"No," said the policeman, "But I need your statements." He walked them over to one of the police cars. They passed the car the Tall Lady had been put in. Neil and Laurie looked at her. They never would have guessed.

THE TIME MACHINE

by George Shea

"What's that, Uncle Fred?" asked Janie.

Uncle Fred was an inventor. He was always building strange things.

"It's my time machine, Janie," he answered. "You step inside it, and it takes you back to the past. It can take you back hundreds, even thousands of years."

"That sounds great," Janie said.

"You could go back to 1776," said Uncle Fred, "and meet George Washington."

"Maybe I could go back to 1492," Janie said. "Then I could watch Columbus land in America. We were just reading about that in school."

"Sure," said Uncle Fred. "Just step inside the machine."

"Are you sure it's safe?" asked Janie. "What if I don't come back?"

"Don't worry," said Uncle Fred. "You will come back all right. You won't be gone more than an hour."

Janie stepped inside the machine.

"Now I'm going to push a few buttons here," Uncle Fred said. He pushed the 1, the 4, the 9, and the 2. "Now I'm going to push the "on" button, Janie, and back you go!"

WOOOOOSSHH!!!

Suddenly everything went white. Janie looked around her. She was on a ship at sea. The ship had big, white sails.

"This is it!" she thought. "I'm back in 1492! This must be the *Santa Maria*, the ship Columbus sailed to America. I wonder where he is?"

A man was coming toward her. He was dressed like an old-time sailor. He had a big, black beard.

"Say, there! Who be ye?" he asked.

"He has a strange way of talking," Janie thought.

"I...I be Janie Wilson," she replied. "Do you...Do ye know where I can find Mr. Columbus?"

"There be no Mr. Columbus on this ship," he replied. "What do ye want here?"

"Isn't this ship the *Santa Maria?*" she asked. "Isn't this the year 1492?"

"Har-har!" the man laughed. "This ship be the *Sea Dog*. This be the year 1592.

And I be Blackbeard the Pirate!"

"Oh, no!" thought Janie. Uncle Fred made a mistake. She was a hundred years too late! And Blackbeard was the meanest pirate that ever sailed the seas!

"Mates!" he called out. Suddenly 20 pirates came out on deck. They were the dirtiest, meanest looking men she had ever seen.

"Do ye have any gold?" Blackbeard asked her. "If ye don't, I'll have ye walk the plank! Har-har!"

"The plank?" asked Janie

"Yes, the plank. I'll have ye feeding the sharks! Now, do ye have any gold?"

Janie thought fast. She looked around. She saw that the ship was near some land. "I don't have any gold with me," she said. "But I know where there is some. There is some gold buried over there," she said pointing.

Blackbeard looked hard at her. "I hope ye be talking true," he said. "If not ye will walk the plank."

Janie wished she were back with Uncle Fred. This was not funny. Then she remembered that Uncle Fred said she would be gone only an hour. She had to fool them for an hour.

They got into a little boat and rowed to the land.

"Now where be the gold?" yelled Blackbeard.

"It is a long way from here," Janie answered. She wanted to use up time. She had to keep them busy looking for the gold.

They walked and walked. An hour went by. But she was still there! Something was wrong, very wrong.

Blackbeard was angry now. "Where be the gold?" he said. "I'm tired of walking."

"It—it's right here," said Janie. She pointed to a spot on the ground.

The pirates started digging. Down, down they went. An hour later, all there was was a big, empty hole. Blackbeard was very angry. "Now ye walk the plank!" he said.

They rowed back to the ship. Janie's heart was beating fast.

"Har-har! On the plank ye go," yelled Blackbeard. He made Janie get on the plank. It hung over the cold water.

"Now—walk!" he told her. He gave her a little push with his sword.

Janie took a step. Then she took another. Three more steps and she would be in the sea. She looked down. She could see the sharks. They were waiting for her.

She took one more step...then another. "Uncle Fred!" she called. "Save me!"

Then Blackbeard gave her another little push, and down she went. She was screaming and falling. Suddenly her feet felt wet and cold. Then everything went white again.

She was back with Uncle Fred.

"I'm sorry, Janie," said Uncle Fred. "I could not get you back as soon as I thought I could."

"You got me back just in time," said Janie. She looked down at her wet shoes.

"Where would you like to go now?" asked Uncle Fred.

"Home to bed," said Janie.